starting to read

©2017 Alligator Products Ltd

Published by Alligator Products Ltd

2nd Floor, 314 Regents Park Road, London N3 2JX

Printed in China   0525

Say hello to Sam

Hello! Here I am. My name is Sam. I like jam and ham and my sister in her pram.

ham   jam

Draw a line under the 'am' sounds in these words.

ambulance

Trace the dotted letters then colour in the 'am' sound.

ram

Sam

j**am**

h**am**

pr**am**

trampoline

3

Scat the cat

Hello! I am Scat the fat cat. I like rats and my cowboy hat.

rattle

Draw a line under the 'at' sounds in these words.

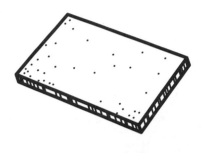

mat

Trace the dotted letters then colour in the 'at' sound.

bat

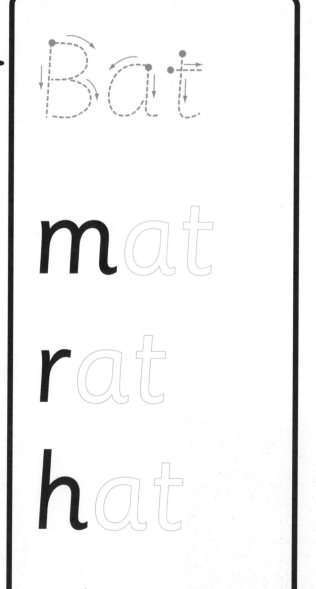

Bat

m at

r at

h at

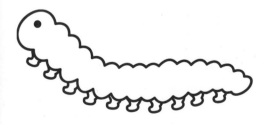

caterpillar

Counting Ken

Hello! My name is Ken, I like my tent and counting to ten.

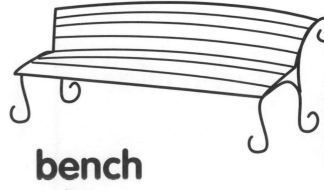

bench

Draw a line under the 'en' sounds in these words.

You're so clever!

hen

Trace the dotted letters then colour in the 'en' sound.

pen

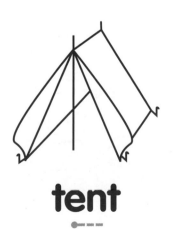

tent

Ken

hen

pen

tent

Meet the vet

Hello! I am the vet to help your pet.

petals

Draw a line under the 'et' sounds in these words.

You're so smart!

kettle

Trace the dotted letters then colour in the 'et' sound.

jet

Vet

jet

net

pet

net

9

Fast fish

Hello! I am a fish with a big tail fin. When I race I like to win!

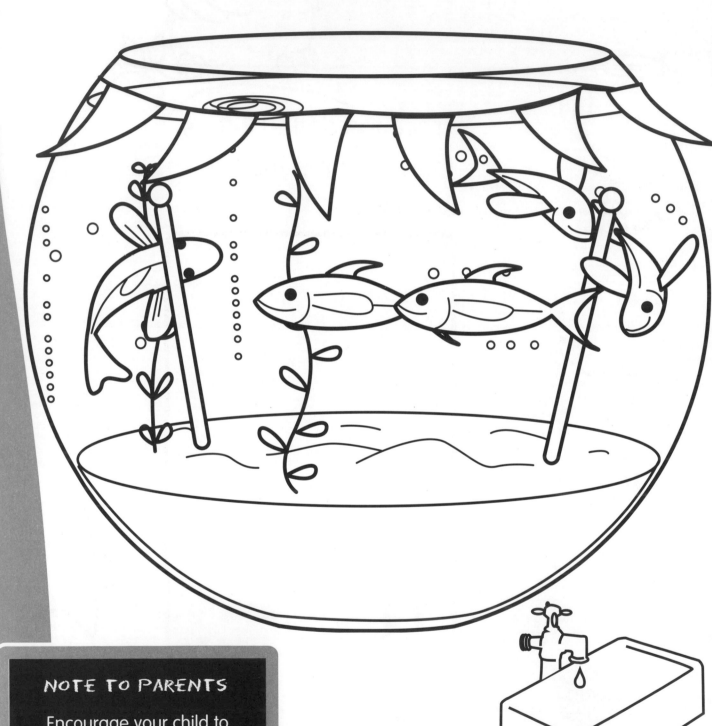

sink

Draw a line under the 'in' sounds in these words.

You're so clever!

bin

pin

tin

ring

Trace the dotted letters then colour in the 'in' sound.

Fin

bin

pin

tin

Happy hippopotamus

Hello! I am a hippo called Pip.
I love the river… drip, drip, drip.

ripple

Draw a line under the 'ip' sounds in these words.

lips

Trace the dotted letters then colour in the 'ip' sound.

zip

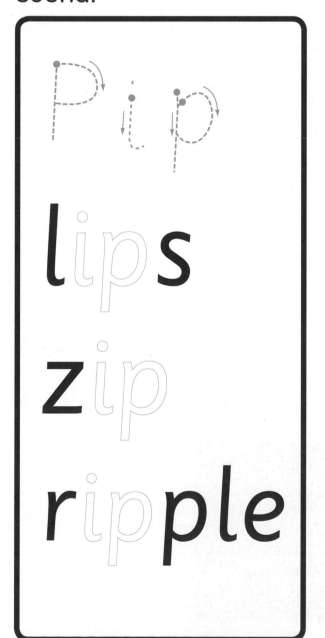

Pip

l**ip**s

z**ip**

r**ip**ple

pip

Frank the frog

Hello! I am Frank the frog.
I can hop from log to log.

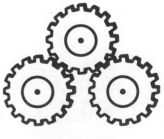

cogs

Draw a line under the 'og' sounds in these words.

You're so smart!

dog

Trace the dotted letters then colour in the 'og' sound.

jog

Frog

d og

j og

h og

hog

Baby Dot

Hello! I am a tiny tot.
I like my cosy cot.

hot water bottle

Draw a line under the 'ot' sounds in these words.

You're so clever!

spotty potty

Trace the dotted letters then colour in the 'ot' sound.

bottle

Dot

sp**ot**

p**ot**ty

b**ot**tle

cotton blanket

Bella bug

Hello! I am Bella the bug on a rug. But I am never in a mug or a jug.

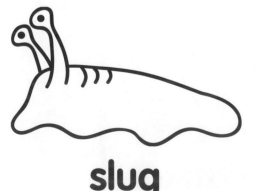

slug

Draw a line under the 'ug' sounds in these words.

hug

Trace the dotted letters then colour in the 'ug' sound.

juggle

Bug

r**ug**

m**ug**

ju**ug**gle

tug boat

Bobble bunny

Hello! I am Bobble bunny. I like having fun.
My friends come to run and play in the sun.

Rapunzel

Draw a line under the 'un' sounds in these words.

What an expert!

A nun

jungle

Trace the dotted letters then colour in the 'un' sound.

Bunny

nun

jungle

bun

bun

The Ark

Here we are at Noah's Ark. Find a shark and a dog that barks.

lark

22

Draw a line under the 'ark' sounds in these words.

park

dark

market

Very good!

Trace the dotted letters then colour in the 'ark' sound.

Ark

sh**ark**

b**ark**

p**ark**

23

Sh, sh, sh

Match the words which have 'sh' at the beginning.
Then match the words which have 'sh' at the end.

wish　　**sheep**

shoes　　**fish**

brush

Excellent!

sheep

Trace the dotted letters then colour in the 'sh' sound.

wish

Sheep

shoes

brush

wish

dish

ship

brush

Colours and shapes

Read the colour label for each shape
below – then start colouring!

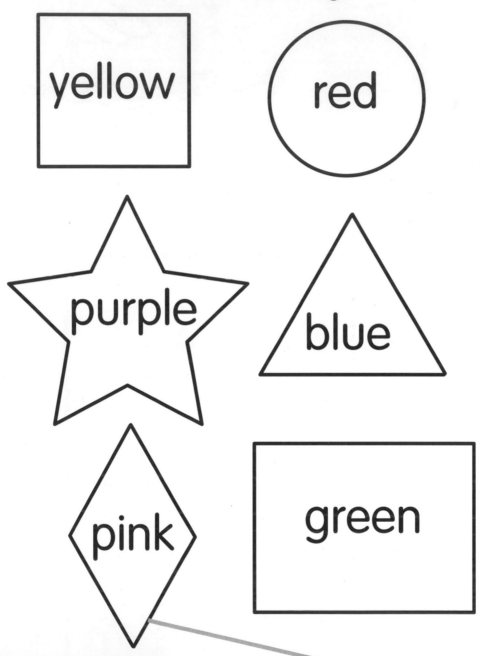

yellow

red

purple

blue

pink

green

NOTE TO PARENTS

Multi-tasking…
matching by colour, shape
and word recognition.

Match the shapes on this page to the shapes opposite. We did the pink diamond for you.

Well done!

27

Happy endings

Hello! I am a king and I like to sing
on my garden swing.

NOTE TO PARENTS

Word association skills – ring and finger go together. Don't forget to look for rhyming endings.

string

Draw a line under the 'ing' sounds in these words.

You're so clever

ring

Trace the dotted letters then colour in the 'ing' sound.

wing

King

s**ing**

sw**ing**

f**ing**er

finger

29

Word pair game

Match the pairs of words. How many can you find?

pen

ambulance

hen

tent

jet

mat

ram

fish

hen

kettle

jet

bat

ship

trampoline

petals

Now it is time for us to be leaving, you have made a great start to RHYMING AND READING!

fish

net

mat

ship

tent

ram

shoes

bat

trampoline

pen

shoes

net

ambulance

kettle

petals

Very
good!